BRAHMS

Songs of Love

LIEBESLIEDER   **OPUS 52**

waltzes for piano duet, with optional SATB voices

English words by W. G. Rothery

VOCAL PART

Performances of this arrangement should be given with the original
piano duet accompaniment, which is available on sale. The piano solo
version is for rehearsal purposes only.

Order No: NOV 070066

NOVELLO PUBLISHING LIMITED
8/9 Frith Street, London W1V 5TZ

SONGS OF LOVE.

(LIEBESLIEDER.)

I.

Johannes Brahms, Op. 52.

II.

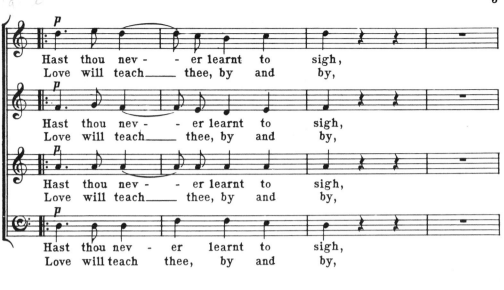

Hast thou nev - - er learnt to sigh,
Love will teach____ thee, by and by,

Hast thou nev - - er learnt to sigh,
Love will teach____ thee, by and by,

Think - ing on ____ the mor - - - row?
Love will bring____ thee sor - - - - row.

III.

TENOR.

O ye maid-ens! you en-chain me, Though so

BASS.

O ye maid-ens! you en-chain me, Though so

oft - en you dis-dain me, But for you I'd be a

oft - en you dis-dain me, But for you I'd be a

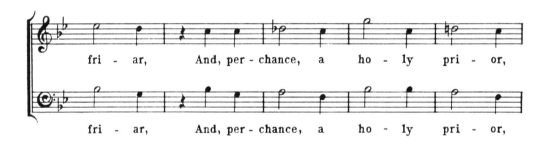

fri - ar, And, per-chance, a ho - ly pri - or,

fri - ar, And, per-chance, a ho - ly pri - or,

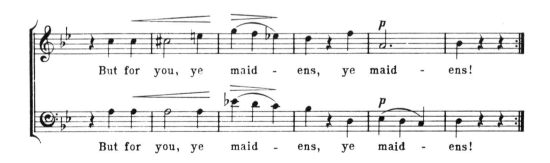

But for you, ye maid - ens, ye maid - ens!

But for you, ye maid - ens, ye maid - ens!

IV.

SOPRANO.

Would that I,— a maid - en

ALTO.

Would that I,— a maid - en

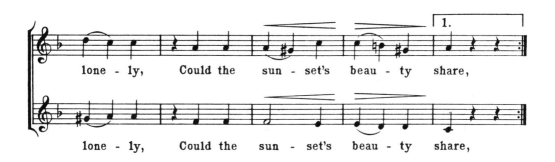

lone - ly, Could the sun - set's beau - ty share,

lone - ly, Could the sun - set's beau - ty share,

share, Giv - ing joy— to one, one on - ly,

espress.

share, Giv - ing joy— to one, one on - ly,

espress.

Life would then be ev - er fair. fair.

Life would then be ev - er fair. fair.

V.

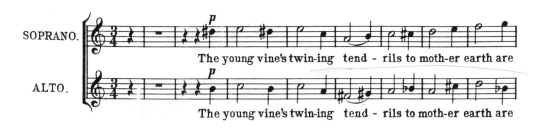

SOPRANO.

The young vine's twin-ing tend - rils to moth-er earth are

ALTO.

The young vine's twin-ing tend - rils to moth-er earth are

droop-ing low.—

droop-ing low.—

TENOR.

I see a ten-der maid - en, whose tears in si-lence flow;

BASS.

I see a ten-der maid - en, whose tears in si-lence flow;

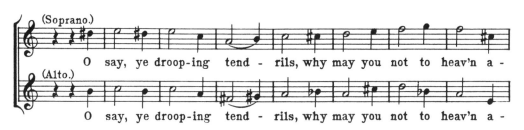

(Soprano.)

O say, ye droop-ing tend - rils, why may you not to heav'n a -

(Alto.)

O say, ye droop-ing tend - rils, why may you not to heav'n a -

-rise?—

-rise?—

(Tenor.)

O tell me, ten - der maid - en, why tears be - dew your eyes?

(Bass.)

O tell me, ten - der maid - en, why tears be - dew your eyes?

(Soprano.)

How can the ten-der branch-es grow heav'n-ward with no

(Alto.)

How can the ten-der branch-es grow heav'n-ward with no

strength___ or stay? And how can a maid be

strength___ or stay? And how can a maid be

(Tenor.)

And how can a maid___ be

(Bass.)

And how can a maid be

hap - py when her dear love's a - way? How

hap - py when her dear love's a - way? How

hap - py when her dear love's a - way?

hap - py when her dear love's a - way?

VI.

TENOR. **Grazioso.**

A ti - ny bird that flew so high one day, Es-

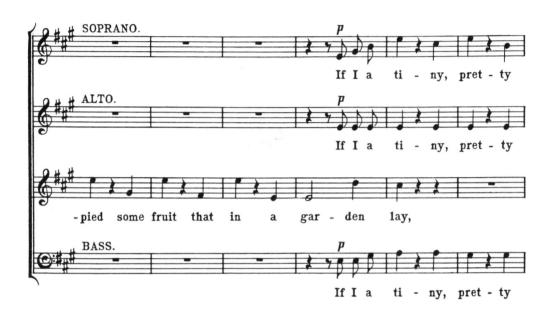

SOPRANO.

If I a ti - ny, pret - ty

ALTO.

If I a ti - ny, pret - ty

-pied some fruit that in a gar - den lay,

BASS.

If I a ti - ny, pret - ty

bird could be, Far would I fly that gar - den fair to see.

bird could be, Far would I fly that gar - den fair to see.

bird could be, Far would I fly that gar - den fair to see.

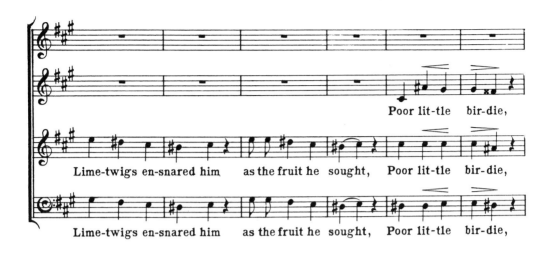

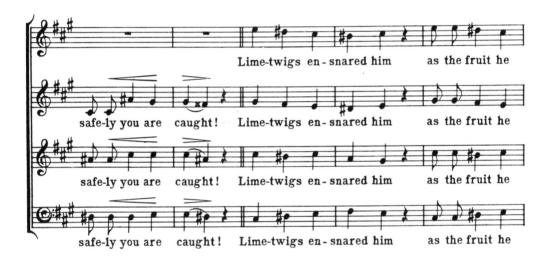

12

you're caught, you're caught!

caught! you're caught, you're caught! If

caught! you're caught, you're caught!

I a ti-ny bird could ev-er be, I'd tar-ry here, and

If I a ti-ny bird could ev-er be, I'd tar-ry

If I a ti-ny bird could ev-er be, I'd tar-ry

not be caught as he,

If I a ti-ny bird could ev-er be, I'd tar-ry

here, and not be caught as he, not as he, not as he,

here, and not be caught as he, not as he, not as

not as he, not as he, not as

here, and not be caught as he, not as he,

not as he, as he. 2

he, not as he, as he.

he, as he. 2 A_ la - dy's

not as he, as he.

A_ la - dy's hand held fast that ti - ny bird,__

A la - dy's hand held fast that ti - ny bird,__

hand, a la - dy's hand held fast that ti - ny bird,__

A la - dy's hand held fast that ti - ny bird,__

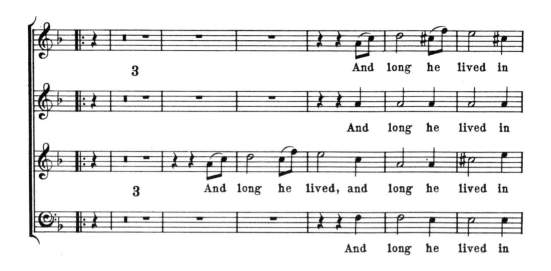

3 And long he lived in

And long he lived in

3 And long he lived, and long he lived in

And long he lived in

hap - pi - ness, I've heard._ 2

hap - pi - ness, I've heard._

hap - pi - ness, I've heard._ 2 If I a

hap - pi - ness, I've heard._

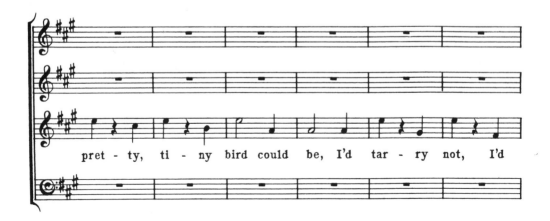

pret - ty, ti - ny bird could be, I'd tar - ry not, I'd

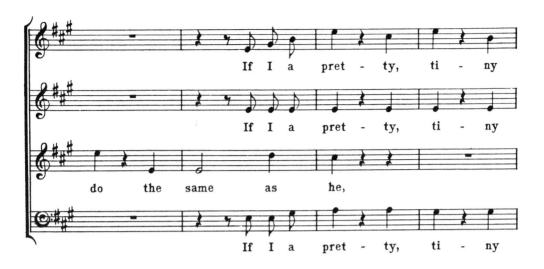

VII.

SOPRANO.
(ALTO.)

How fair the May when vows were
plight-ed, How sweet was life_ with love_ u - nit - ed, We
vow'd that naught our troth could sev - er, His heart_ was
mine, mine his_ for ev - er. Ah, love de-
-ceiv - ing, His vows for - got - ten 'ere May_ was
dead He left me griev - ing, My_ heart is
bro-ken, my hope_____ hath fled.

Repeat

VIII.

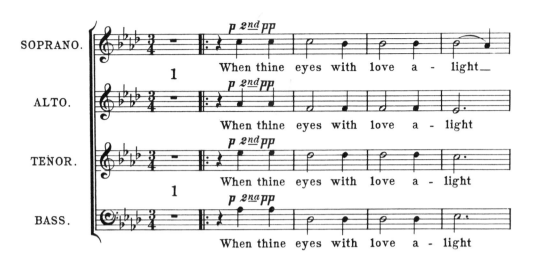

SOPRANO.

When thine eyes with love a - light

ALTO.

When thine eyes with love a - light

TENOR.

When thine eyes with love a - light

BASS.

When thine eyes with love a - light

With fond hope en - due me, All my trou-bles

With fond hope en - due me, All my trou-bles

With fond hope en - due me, All my trou-bles

With fond hope en - due me, All my trou-bles

take to flight, Cares no more pur - sue me;

take to flight, Cares no more pur - sue me;

take to flight, Cares no more pur - sue me;

take to flight, Cares no more pur - sue me;

Keep that ten - der flame a - glow,

Keep that ten - der flame____ a - glow,

Keep that ten - der flame a - glow, Keep its

Keep that ten - der flame a - glow, Keep its

Keep its light un - dy - ing, Ne'er such love as

Keep its light un - dy - ing, Ne'er such love as

light un - dy - ing, Ne'er such love as

light un - dy - ing, Ne'er such love as

mine thou'lt know, To_ thy love____ re - ply - ing. 1

mine thou'lt know, To thy love____ re - ply - ing.

mine thou'lt know, To_ thy love____ re - ply - ing. 1

mine thou'lt know, To thy love____ re - ply - ing.

IX.

SOPRANO.

ALTO.
By Dan-ube's wa - ter a

TENOR.
By Dan-ube's wa - ter a

BASS.
By Dan-ube's wa - ter a

house doth stand,— A maid - en dwells there, who

house doth stand,— A maid - en dwells there, who

house doth stand,— A maid - en dwells there, who

waves her hand; Well guard-ed is she,—

waves her hand; Well guard-ed is she,—

waves her hand; Well guard-ed is she,—

that maid - en fair,___ For ten i-ron bars hold her

that maid - en fair,___ For ten i-ron bars hold her

that maid - en fair,___ For ten i-ron bars hold her

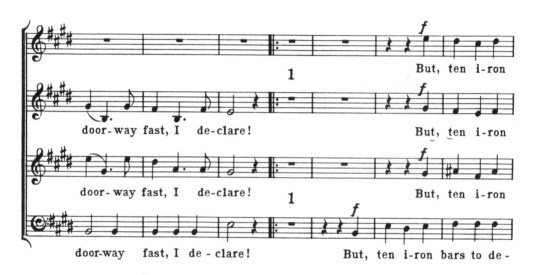

1 But, ten i-ron

door-way fast, I de-clare! But, ten i-ron

door-way fast, I de-clare! *1* But, ten i-ron

door-way fast, I de - clare! But, ten i-ron bars to de-

bars to de - fend a lass, I'll break them as though they were

bars to de - fend a lass, I'll break them as though they were

bars to de - fend a lass, I'll break them as though they were

-fend a lass, I'll break them as though they were

X.

SOPRANO. O__ how soft the stream - let flows,

ALTO. O how soft the stream - let

TENOR. O__ how soft the stream - let

BASS. O how soft the stream - let

38

Through__ the mea - dows wind - - ing;

flows, Through the mea - dows wind - - ing;

flows, Through the mea - dows wind - - ing;

flows, Through the mea - dows wind - - ing;

O__ how sweet, when trust-ing hearts Love for love are

O__ how sweet, when

O__ how sweet, when trust-ing hearts Love for love are find - -

O__ how

XI.

SOPRANO.

No, I can-not bear the gos-sips' pet-ty sto-ries,

ALTO.

No, I can-not bear the gos-sips' pet-ty sto-ries,

TENOR.

No, I can-not tear the gos-sips' pet-ty sto-ries,

BASS.

No, I can-not bear the gos-sips' pet-ty sto-ries,

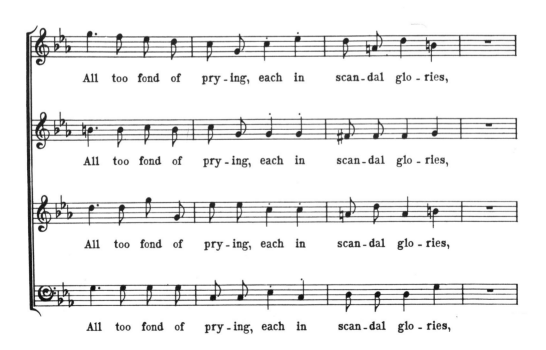

All too fond of pry-ing, each in scan-dal glo-ries,

All too fond of pry-ing, each in scan-dal glo-ries,

All too fond of pry-ing, each in scan-dal glo-ries,

All too fond of pry-ing, each in scan-dal glo-ries,

No, I can-not bear the gos-sips' pet-ty sto-ries, All too fond of

pry-ing, each in scan-dal glo-ries. Am I mer-ry? then, they say, wild

oats I'm sow-ing; Am I dull? With love my brain is sure-ly

go - ing, sure - ly go - ing. No, I can - not

bear the gos - sips' pet - ty sto - ries, All too fond of

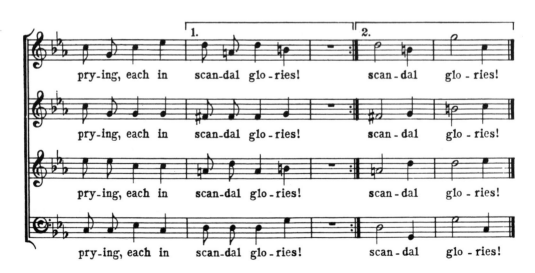

pry - ing, each in scan - dal glo - ries! scan - dal glo - ries!

XII.

SOPRANO. Lock-smith, come, and make me pad-locks, Ma-ny

ALTO. Lock-smith, come, and make me pad-locks, Ma-ny

TENOR. Lock-smith, come, and make me pad-locks, Ma-ny

BASS. Lock-smith, come, and make me pad-locks, Ma-ny

46 (1st time)

pad - locks, pad - locks, trus-ty friend,

pad - locks, pad - locks, trus-ty friend,

pad - locks, pad - locks, trus-ty friend, Then the

pad - locks, pad - locks, trus-ty friend,

Then the gos - sips' lips I'll fet-ter, Sure-ly fet-ter,

Then the gos - sips' lips I'll fet-ter, Sure-ly fet-ter,

gos - sips', Then the gos - sips' lips I'll fet-ter, Sure-ly fet-ter,

Then the gos - sips' lips I'll fet-ter, fet-ter, Sure-ly fet-ter,

XIII.

SOPRANO.

O'er the sea___ the swal-lows fly, the swal - lows fly,

ALTO.

O'er the sea___ the swal-lows fly, the swal - lows fly,

Home-ward, nev - er tir - ing, So the heart for rest doth

Home-ward, nev-er tir - ing, So the heart for rest doth

sigh, Love and peace de - sir - ing, - sir - ing.

sigh, Love and peace de - sir - ing, - sir - ing.

XIV.

TENOR.

1. See how clear the moon-beams play, On the
2. Weave a - round her heart a spell, Mel - low

BASS.

1. See how clear the moon-beams play, On the
2. Weave a - round her heart a spell, Mel - low

bil - lows gleam - ing, In their ra - diant
moon a - bove me, Tell her that I

bil - lows gleam - ing, In their ra - diant
moon a - bove me, Tell her that I

light I stray,___ While my love is dream - ing;
love her well,___ Bid her ev - er love me.

light I stray,___ While my love is dream - ing;
love her well,___ Bid her ev - er love me.

XV.

SOPRANO. Night-in - gale, sing lul - la - bies,

ALTO. Night-in - gale, sing lul - la - bies,

TENOR. Night - in - gale, sing lul - la - bies,

BASS. Night - in - gale, sing lul - la - bies,

When the__ stars are peep - - ing; Dear-est

When the stars are peep - - ing; Dear-est

When the stars are peep - - ing; Dear-est

When the stars are peep - - ing; Dear-est

XVI.

now for re - lease I'm plead - - ing, re - lease I'm

And now for re - lease I'm

And now for re - lease I'm plead - - ing, Be-

And

plead - - ing, Be - moan - ing, be - moan - ing, be - moan -

plead - - ing, Be - moan - ing, be - moan - ing, be - moan -

- moan - - ing, be - moan - ing, be - moan - ing, be - moan -

now for re - lease I'm plead - ing, Be - moan - ing, be - moan -

- ing my griev - ous plight. griev - ous plight.

- ing my griev - ous plight. griev - ous plight.

- ing my griev - ous plight. griev - ous plight.

- ing my griev - ous plight. griev - ous plight.

XVII.

O stray not, dear heart, midst yon-der fair mead-ow way, The flow'rs a - bout thy feet____ will harm thee, so wet are they. O Streamlets o'er-flow-ing path and mead-ow run down the lea, For show'rs of tears mine eyes____ have wept there, For love of thee. Streamlets o'er - flow-ing path and mead-ow run down the lea, For show'rs of tears mine eyes____ have wept there, For love of thee.

XVIII.

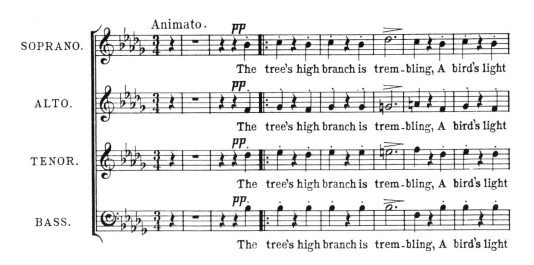

SOPRANO. The tree's high branch is trem-bling, A bird's light

ALTO. The tree's high branch is trem-bling, A bird's light

TENOR. The tree's high branch is trem-bling, A bird's light

BASS. The tree's high branch is trem-bling, A bird's light

wing hath swept it When fly - - ing free,___ when fly -

wing hath swept it When fly - ing free,___ when fly -

wing hath swept it When fly - - ing free,___ when fly -

wing hath swept it When fly - ing free,___ when fly -

- ing free.___ The — And so my heart is trem - bling, My

- ing free.___ The — And so__ my heart is trem - bling, My

- ing free.___ The — And so__ my heart is trem - bling, My

- ing free.___ The — And so my heart is trem - bling, My

ve - ry soul is sha - ken With love and love's sweet sor - row, with

ve - ry soul is sha - ken With love and love's sweet sor - row, with

ve - ry soul is sha - ken With love and love's sweet sor - row, with

ve - ry soul is sha - ken With love and love's sweet sor - row, with

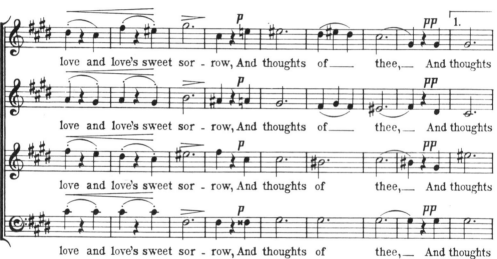

love and love's sweet sor - row, And thoughts of____ thee,__ And thoughts

love and love's sweet sor - row, And thoughts of____ thee,__ And thoughts

love and love's sweet sor - row, And thoughts of thee,__ And thoughts

love and love's sweet sor - row, And thoughts of thee,__ And thoughts

of thee,__ And thoughts of thee.__

of____ thee,__ And thoughts of____ thee.__

of____ thee,__ And thoughts of____ thee.__

of thee, And thoughts of thee.__

Printed and bound in Great Britain by
Caligraving Limited Thetford Norfolk